1986

PIERRE-AUGUSTE RENOIR, 1914
Photograph private collection, Paris

**Published by Harry N. Abrams, Inc., New York,
in association with the Museum of Fine Arts, Boston, and
with reproductions from The Art Institute of Chicago**

ISBN 0-8109-7737-0 (HNA edition only)
Works of art from the collections of the Museum of Fine Arts,
Boston, copyright © 1985 the Museum of Fine Arts, Boston
Works of art from the collections of The Art Institute of Chicago
copyright © 1985 The Art Institute of Chicago
Published by Harry N. Abrams, Inc., New York
Picture reproduction rights reserved by the Museum of Fine Arts,
Boston, and The Art Institute of Chicago
Printed and bound in Japan

Introduction

The magical happiness of Renoir's waltzing couples and the sun-flushed beauty of his bathers have placed his paintings among the most widely recognized and universally loved images in Western art. Together with Monet's shimmering landscapes, Renoir's carefree figures provide the basic definition of Impressionism for casual viewer and scholar alike. But both Renoir and the Impressionist movement he helped create are far more complex than is usually recognized. Café scenes and magnificent nudes may shape Renoir's reputation for today's viewers, but in his own lifetime, it was portraiture that provided his livelihood. And while we now view Renoir as a quintessential Impressionist, his colleagues in that group were sometimes skeptical that he shared their determined commitment to depict modern life directly as they saw it, without idealization or studio artifice.

Nowhere can the brilliance and the contradiction of Renoir's Impressionism be seen so well as in the context of the nineteenth-century collections of the Museum of Fine Arts, Boston, and The Art Institute of Chicago. Through the generous gifts and bequests of enthusiastic nineteenth- and early twentieth-century collectors, who often bought paintings directly from the artists themselves, both museums have assembled Impressionist collections that are famous throughout the world and easily rival the collections in the artists' native Paris.

For unlike so many critical artistic achievements of the past, Impressionism was quite truly the accomplishment of a group of talents, artists often at odds with one another, just as often seated side-by-side before the same motif. Renoir's art was shaped as much by the interests and the abilities of his comrades as by his own relentless thirst for painting. As they worked together, argued together, and cajoled one another into rejoining their often-splintered exhibiting society, Renoir, Monet, Pissarro, and

Cézanne each took from the others new means for expressing the realities of their shared world and at the same time challenged his friends with new motifs or new artistic problems.

As rich as both the Boston and Chicago collections are in Impressionist paintings, each has its own character: if Renoir as a landscape painter can best be enjoyed in Boston, his brilliant scenes of life on the terraces and in the gardens of Paris are better represented in Chicago. There, too, is found the early master-piece of Renoir's friend and patron Gustave Caillebotte, *Paris, A Rainy Day,* while one of that artist's most brilliant later paintings, *Fruit Displayed on a Stand,* brightens the Boston collection. Just as the widely acclaimed international exhibition *Renoir* has in-vited thousands of viewers to look more broadly at this ex-ceptional artist's achievement, so this calendar invites the Im-pressionist admirer to enjoy Renoir's work within the artistic company from whom he borrowed as much as he gave.

Alexandra R. Murphy
Assistant Curator, European Paintings
Museum of Fine Arts, Boston

30
MONDAY

31
TUESDAY

New Year's Eve

1
WEDNESDAY

New Year's Day

2
THURSDAY

3
FRIDAY

4
SATURDAY

5
SUNDAY

DECEMBER

s	m	t	w	t	f	s
	1	2	3	4	5	6	7
8	9	10	11	12	13	14
15	16	17	18	19	20	21
22	23	24	25	26	27	28
29	30	31

JANUARY

s	m	t	w	t	f	s
			1	2	3	4
5	6	7	8	9	10	11
12	13	14	15	16	17	18
19	20	21	22	23	24	25
26	27	28	29	30	31

RENOIR
Algerian Girl.   1881
Oil on canvas
BOSTON

Even before Renoir's visit
to Algeria in 1881, his
attention had been drawn
to the elaborate costumes
and brilliant colors of
North Africa by the
Moroccan paintings of
Delacroix. This small,
jewel-like painting dating
from Renoir's own travels
in Africa emphasizes the
rich patterns and striking
hues of the young woman's
dress and surroundings.

JANUARY

s	m	t	w	t	f	s
			1	2	3	4
5	6	7	8	9	10	11
12	13	14	15	16	17	18
19	20	21	22	23	24	25
26	27	28	29	30	31	

RENOIR
Lady Sewing. 1879
Oil on canvas
CHICAGO

Renoir's redheaded model, Margot, was probably the sitter for this intimate canvas whose subject matter resembles that of Pissarro, while the brushstroke shows the strong influence of Monet. *Lady Sewing* was painted in 1879, while the Impressionist group was still reasonably close.

6

MONDAY

7

TUESDAY

8

WEDNESDAY

9

THURSDAY

10

FRIDAY

11

SATURDAY

12

SUNDAY

13
MONDAY

14
TUESDAY

15
WEDNESDAY

Martin Luther King, Jr.'s Birthday

16
THURSDAY

17
FRIDAY

18
SATURDAY

19
SUNDAY

JANUARY
s	m	t	w	t	f	s
				1	2	3	4
5	6	7	8	9	10	11
12	13	14	15	16	17	18
19	20	21	22	23	24	25
26	27	28	29	30	31	

MONET
Snow at Argenteuil.
About 1874
Oil on canvas
BOSTON

Although Monet and Renoir frequently worked together in the early years of Impressionism, Monet was never successful in convincing his friend of the pleasures of painting overcast days or wintry scenes. The beauty of the damp, snow-veiled route to Argenteuil completely escaped Renoir, who could envision only wet feet and numb fingers.

JANUARY

s	m	t	w	t	f	s
				1	2	3	4
5	6	7	8	9	10	11
12	13	14	15	16	17	18
19	20	21	22	23	24	25
26	27	28	29	30	31	

TOULOUSE-LAUTREC
At the Moulin Rouge.
1892
Oil on canvas
CHICAGO

With its risqué floor show
featuring the cancan, the
Moulin Rouge attracted an
older, more dissolute
clientele than frequented
the cafés associated
with the Impressionist
generation. Lautrec
captures the café's
ambience with caricatural
figures and the acidic colors
of gaslight.

20
MONDAY

21
TUESDAY

22
WEDNESDAY

23
THURSDAY

24
FRIDAY

25
SATURDAY

26
SUNDAY

27
MONDAY

28
TUESDAY

29
WEDNESDAY

30
THURSDAY

31
FRIDAY

1
SATURDAY

2
SUNDAY

JANUARY

s	m	t	w	t	f	s
				1	2	3	4
5	6	7	8	9	10	11
12	13	14	15	16	17	18
19	20	21	22	23	24	25
26	27	28	29	30	31

FEBRUARY

s	m	t	w	t	f	s
						1
2	3	4	5	6	7	8
9	10	11	12	13	14	15
16	17	18	19	20	21	22
23	24	25	26	27	28

DEGAS
Dancer. About 1878
Pastel on paper
BOSTON

Degas's paintings and
pastels of ballet dancers in
performance, at rehearsal,
or relaxing between stage
flats enabled him to study
the human form in a
myriad of poses, both
natural and full of artifice.
For Renoir, dance was
a more social activity,
a record of the
entertainments and
interactions of his friends
and social circle.

FEBRUARY

s	m	t	w	t	f	s
						1
2	3	4	5	6	7	8
9	10	11	12	13	14	15
16	17	18	19	20	21	22
23	24	25	26	27	28	

FANTIN-LATOUR
*Flowers and Fruit on a
Table.*   1865
Oil on canvas
BOSTON

Fantin-Latour was a close
friend of Renoir and Monet
during their student days,
and he shared their interest
in still lifes composed of
simple garden flowers and
everyday fruits. But while
they soon gave themselves
up to figure subjects and
landscapes, Fantin-Latour
went on to become one of
the greatest still-life
painters of the nineteenth
century.

3
MONDAY

4
TUESDAY

5
WEDNESDAY

6
THURSDAY

7
FRIDAY

8
SATURDAY

9
SUNDAY

10
MONDAY

FEBRUARY
s m t w t f s
                    1
2 3 4 5 6 7 8
9 10 11 12 13 14 15
16 17 18 19 20 21 22
23 24 25 26 27 28

11
TUESDAY

12
WEDNESDAY

Lincoln's Birthday
Ash Wednesday

RENOIR
Dance at Bougival.   1883
Oil on canvas
BOSTON

In the 1880s, Renoir became determined to return the human figure to central importance in Impressionist painting. For the painting that marks this crucial turning point, Renoir persuaded his brother Edouard and a friend and model, Suzanne Valadon, to pose as a couple dancing at an outdoor café-dance hall frequented by young Parisians.

13
THURSDAY

14
FRIDAY

St. Valentine's Day

15
SATURDAY

16
SUNDAY

FEBRUARY

s	m	t	w	t	f	s
						1
2	3	4	5	6	7	8
9	10	11	12	13	14	15
16	17	18	19	20	21	22
23	24	25	26	27	28	

RENOIR
Dance at Bougival.   1883
Oil on canvas
BOSTON

While the central couple in
Dance at Bougival is very
carefully rendered, Renoir
maintained his looser, more
spontaneous brushwork for
the background figures and
landscape details.

Washington's Birthday Observed

17
MONDAY

18
TUESDAY

19
WEDNESDAY

20
THURSDAY

21
FRIDAY

Washington's Birthday

22
SATURDAY

23
SUNDAY

24
MONDAY

25
TUESDAY

26
WEDNESDAY

27
THURSDAY

28
FRIDAY

1
SATURDAY

2
SUNDAY

FEBRUARY

s	m	t	w	t	f	s
						1
2	3	4	5	6	7	8
9	10	11	12	13	14	15
16	17	18	19	20	21	22
23	24	25	26	27	28	

MARCH

s	m	t	w	t	f	s
						1
2	3	4	5	6	7	8
9	10	11	12	13	14	15
16	17	18	19	20	21	22
23	24	25	26	27	28	29
30	31					

MANET
The Street Singer.   1862
Oil on canvas
BOSTON

Manet was ten years older than most of the Impressionists, and one of their especial heroes. His interest in modern costume, in unidealized realism, and in a spontaneous, heavy brushwork—all set forth in *The Street Singer* of 1862—helped define the principal problems that would occupy French artists for nearly thirty years.

MARCH

s	m	t	w	t	f	s
						1
2	3	4	5	6	7	8
9	10	11	12	13	14	15
16	17	18	19	20	21	22
23	24	25	26	27	28	29
30	31					

MONET
*Boulevard St.-Denis,
Argenteuil, in Winter.*
1875
Oil on canvas
BOSTON

Just across from the
suburban train depot, this
pink house with green-blue
shutters was rented by
Monet during 1874–76.
Most Impressionist snow
scenes were painted close to
the artists' homes, or to
those of friends, probably
so they could periodically
warm stiff fingers or damp
feet—drawbacks that
failed to dim Monet's
commitment to natural
light effects.

3
MONDAY

4
TUESDAY

5
WEDNESDAY

6
THURSDAY

7
FRIDAY

8
SATURDAY

9
SUNDAY

10
MONDAY

11
TUESDAY

12
WEDNESDAY

13
THURSDAY

14
FRIDAY

15
SATURDAY

16
SUNDAY

MARCH

s	m	t	w	t	f	s
						1
2	3	4	5	6	7	8
9	10	11	12	13	14	15
16	17	18	19	20	21	22
23	24	25	26	27	28	29
30	31					

RENOIR
Two Little Circus Girls.
1879
Oil on canvas
CHICAGO

The circus was a familiar part of the work of Renoir's contemporaries Jean-Louis Forain and, later, Henri de Toulouse-Lautrec. In 1868, Renoir had painted *The Clown* and, eleven years later, two young sisters, Francisca and Angelina Wartenberg, jugglers in the Circus Fernando. Their blue and gold costumes contrast with the vivid oranges, which were thrown to the girls by exuberant spectators at the close of their act.

MARCH

s	m	t	w	t	f	s
						1
2	3	4	5	6	7	8
9	10	11	12	13	14	15
16	17	18	19	20	21	22
23	24	25	26	27	28	29
30	31					

RENOIR
*Madame Clapisson (Lady
with a Fan).* 1883
Oil on canvas
CHICAGO

Although Renoir had to
paint another version of
his portrait of Madame
Clapisson before this, the
second, was accepted, he
took obvious delight in her
round, luxuriant form and
creamy skin, as well as the
opulence of her gold
bangles, yellow kid gloves,
and ostrich-feather fan.

17
St. Patrick's Day
MONDAY

18
TUESDAY

19
WEDNESDAY

20
THURSDAY

21
FRIDAY

22
SATURDAY

23
Palm Sunday
SUNDAY

24
MONDAY

25
TUESDAY

26
WEDNESDAY

27
THURSDAY

28
FRIDAY   Good Friday

29
SATURDAY

30
SUNDAY   Easter Sunday

MARCH
s m t w t f s
                   1
2 3 4 5 6 7 8
9 10 11 12 13 14 15
16 17 18 19 20 21 22
23 24 25 26 27 28 29
30 31

RENOIR
Rocky Crags at L'Estaque.
1882
Oil on canvas
BOSTON

After returning from Italy
in 1882, Renoir stayed for
a short time in the south
of France, visiting and
working alongside
Cézanne. His landscapes
from this trip reflect
Cézanne's impact in their
fascination with the rough,
rocky barrenness of the
hillsides.

MARCH

s	m	t	w	t	f	s
						1
2	3	4	5	6	7	8
9	10	11	12	13	14	15
16	17	18	19	20	21	22
23	24	25	26	27	28	29
30	31					

APRIL

s	m	t	w	t	f	s
		1	2	3	4	5
6	7	8	9	10	11	12
13	14	15	16	17	18	19
20	21	22	23	24	25	26
27	28	29	30			

MONET
Rouen Cathedral at Dawn.
1894
Oil on canvas
BOSTON

Renoir moved away from
the Impressionist fidelity to
nature and the celebration
of transient effects of light
or weather because he
feared exactly the
disintegration of three-
dimensional form that most
entranced Monet. The
great cathedral series of
1893–94 demonstrates
Monet's subordination of
the immortal monument to
patterns of light and color.

31
MONDAY

1
TUESDAY

2
WEDNESDAY

3
THURSDAY

4
FRIDAY

5
SATURDAY

6
SUNDAY

7
MONDAY

8
TUESDAY

9
WEDNESDAY

10
THURSDAY

11
FRIDAY

12
SATURDAY

13
SUNDAY

APRIL

s m t w t f s
        1 2 3 4 5
 6 7 8 9 10 11 12
13 14 15 16 17 18 19
20 21 22 23 24 25 26
27 28 29 30

CAILLEBOTTE
*Paris, A Rainy Day
(Intersection of the Rue de
Turin and Rue de
Moscou).* 1877
Oil on canvas
CHICAGO

Slightly younger than
the main Impressionist
generation, Caillebotte
joined their second group
show, in 1876. He quickly
became an active
participant and, with
inherited wealth, a
generous patron. His
paintings frequently
celebrate the architecture
and commerce of the Paris
boulevards at their most
modern extremes.

APRIL

s	m	t	w	t	f	s
		1	2	3	4	5
6	7	8	9	10	11	12
13	14	15	16	17	18	19
20	21	22	23	24	25	26
27	28	29	30			

PISSARRO
Poultry Market at Gisors.
1885
Gouache and black chalk
on paper mounted on
canvas
BOSTON

Renoir and Pissarro were
both intrigued by the color
possibilities of matte media
like pastel and gouache.
Chalks and opaque
watercolors also allowed
both artists more
opportunity for drawing
with their colors than they
found possible with the
more fluid oil medium.

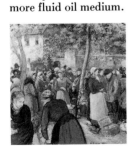

14
MONDAY

15
TUESDAY

16
WEDNESDAY

17
THURSDAY

18
FRIDAY

19
SATURDAY

20
SUNDAY

21
MONDAY

22
TUESDAY

23
WEDNESDAY

Passover Begins (Sundown)

24
THURSDAY

25
FRIDAY

26
SATURDAY

27
SUNDAY

Daylight Saving Begins

APRIL

s	m	t	w	t	f	s
		1	2	3	4	5
6	7	8	9	10	11	12
13	14	15	16	17	18	19
20	21	22	23	24	25	26
27	28	29	30			

DEGAS
Race Horses at Longchamp.
About 1873–75
Oil on canvas
BOSTON

Degas shared Renoir's interest in the leisure activities that were most typical of their own age— whether for one it was horse racing, and for the other, sailing parties and the suburban café-cum-dance hall. Living through a period of extraordinary prosperity and change, they believed they had an important artistic responsibility to be true to their own time.

APRIL

s	m	t	w	t	f	s
		1	2	3	4	5
6	7	8	9	10	11	12
13	14	15	16	17	18	19
20	21	22	23	24	25	26
27	28	29	30			

MAY

s	m	t	w	t	f	s
				1	2	3
4	5	6	7	8	9	10
11	12	13	14	15	16	17
18	19	20	21	22	23	24
25	26	27	28	29	30	31

RENOIR
The Boating Couple.
About 1881
Pastel on paper
BOSTON

The beauty of the Seine just a few miles north of Paris made sailing and renting small rowboats or sculls popular leisure activities for young people escaping the crush of the city on weekends and holidays. As Renoir carefully recorded, new styles in hats and dress were introduced to complement the new activities.

28
MONDAY

29
TUESDAY

30
WEDNESDAY

1
THURSDAY

2
FRIDAY

3
SATURDAY

4
SUNDAY

5
MONDAY

6
TUESDAY

7
WEDNESDAY

8
THURSDAY

9
FRIDAY

10
SATURDAY

11
SUNDAY

Mother's Day

MAY

s	m	t	w	t	f	s
				1	2	3
4	5	6	7	8	9	10
11	12	13	14	15	16	17
18	19	20	21	22	23	24
25	26	27	28	29	30	31

MONET
Monet's House at Argenteuil. 1873
Oil on canvas
CHICAGO

Monet moved to Argenteuil, just a fifteen-minute train ride from Paris proper, in 1871; and his comfortable rented home and garden became a popular working site for visiting friends, notably Renoir and Manet. His wife, Camille, and their young son, Jean, were often called upon to pose for members of the group.

MAY

s	m	t	w	t	f	s
				1	2	3
4	5	6	7	8	9	10
11	12	13	14	15	16	17
18	19	20	21	22	23	24
25	26	27	28	29	30	31

RENOIR
On the Terrace.   1881
Oil on canvas
CHICAGO

A young woman, possibly
the actress Mlle. Darlaud,
and a little girl who has yet
to be identified are depicted
on the terrace of the
Restaurant Fournaise in the
fashionable Parisian suburb
of Chatou. Renoir was
particularly adept at
creating posed scenes that
carry a convincing air of
reality.

12
MONDAY

13
TUESDAY

14
WEDNESDAY

15
THURSDAY

16
FRIDAY

Armed Forces Day

17
SATURDAY

18
SUNDAY

19

MONDAY

20

TUESDAY

21

WEDNESDAY

22

THURSDAY

23

FRIDAY

24

SATURDAY

25

SUNDAY

MAY

s	m	t	w	t	f	s
					1	2	3
4	5	6	7	8	9	10
11	12	13	14	15	16	17
18	19	20	21	22	23	24
25	26	27	28	29	30	31

PISSARRO
Woman and Child at the Well. 1882
Oil on canvas
CHICAGO

Pissarro, like Renoir, took great interest in the lives of the women and children around him. However, as an artist, he was more often drawn to the rural lifestyle of peasants, in contrast to Renoir, who chose to study the new suburban class developing on the edges of Paris.

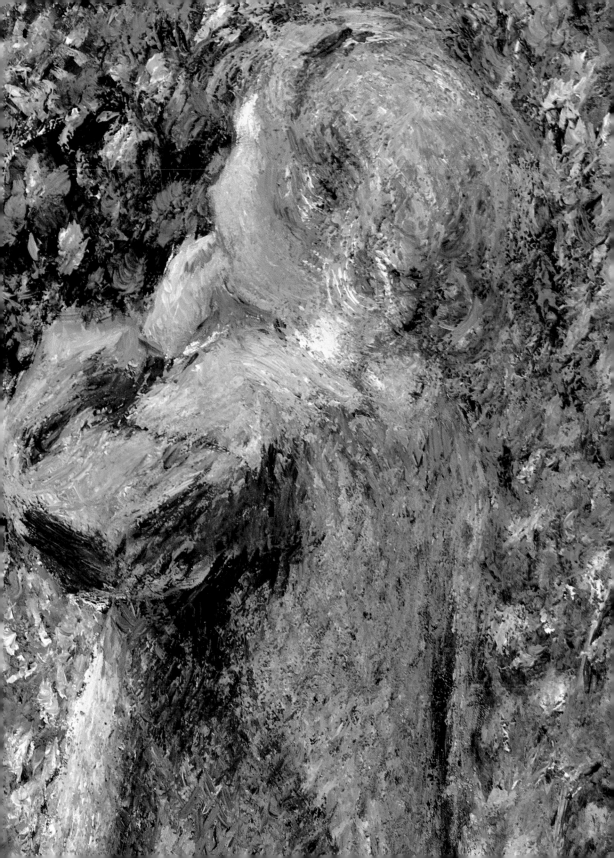

MAY

s	m	t	w	t	f	s
				1	2	3
4	5	6	7	8	9	10
11	12	13	14	15	16	17
18	19	20	21	22	23	24
25	26	27	28	29	30	31

JUNE

s	m	t	w	t	f	s
1	2	3	4	5	6	7
8	9	10	11	12	13	14
15	16	17	18	19	20	21
22	23	24	25	26	27	28
29	30					

SEURAT
Sunday Afternoon on the Island of La Grande-Jatte. 1884–86
Oil on canvas
CHICAGO

Excited by the bright colors of Impressionism but disturbed by the loss of three-dimensional solidity that went with Impressionist brushwork, a younger group of artists, led by Seurat, experimented with a technique of tiny, controlled dots of color that could be shaped more easily into monumental forms and figures.

26
MONDAY

Memorial Day Observed

27
TUESDAY

28
WEDNESDAY

29
THURSDAY

30
FRIDAY

Memorial Day

31
SATURDAY

1
SUNDAY

2

MONDAY

3

TUESDAY

4

WEDNESDAY

5

THURSDAY

6

FRIDAY

7

SATURDAY

8

SUNDAY

JUNE

s	m	t	w	t	f	s
	1	2	3	4	5	6	7
8	9	10	11	12	13	14
15	16	17	18	19	20	21
22	23	24	25	26	27	28
29	30					

MONET
*Camille Monet and a Child
in the Artist's Garden in
Argenteuil.* 1875
Oil on canvas
BOSTON

Painted under Renoir's
influence, this view of
Monet's wife in the family
garden has a delicacy in
fleshtones and portrait
details that is seldom found
in Monet's work.

JUNE

s m t w t f s
1 2 3 4 5 6 7
8 9 10 11 12 13 14
15 16 17 18 19 20 21
22 23 24 25 26 27 28
29 30

RENOIR
Woman with a Parasol and a Small Child on a Sunlit Hillside. About 1874
Oil on canvas
BOSTON

During the early years of Impressionism, Renoir often visited Monet and his family in Argenteuil, outside Paris. Working together, the two artists profoundly affected each other's style. This sparkling summer image of Camille Monet displays an assertive, feathery brushwork more typical of her husband's work than of Renoir's.

9
MONDAY

10
TUESDAY

11
WEDNESDAY

12
THURSDAY

13
FRIDAY

Flag Day

14
SATURDAY

Father's Day

15
SUNDAY

16
MONDAY

17
TUESDAY

18
WEDNESDAY

19
THURSDAY

20
FRIDAY

21
SATURDAY

22
SUNDAY

JUNE

s m t w t f s
      1 2 3 4 5 6 7
8 9 10 11 12 13 14
15 16 17 18 19 20 21
22 23 24 25 26 27 28
29 30

RENOIR
Alfred Sisley.
About 1875–76
Oil on canvas
CHICAGO

Renoir met his fellow
painter Alfred Sisley when
they were both students in
Charles Gleyre's studio.
Sisley sat for Renoir on
several occasions, and here
Renoir has posed his friend
informally, focusing the
composition on Sisley's
expressive features.

JUNE

s	m	t	w	t	f	s
	1	2	3	4	5	6	7
8	9	10	11	12	13	14
15	16	17	18	19	20	21
22	23	24	25	26	27	28
29	30					

BOUDIN
*Beach Scene with
Fashionably Dressed
Figures.*   1865
Oil on panel
BOSTON

Boudin was older than the
Impressionists, and had
no formal ties to the
Impressionist group. But as
the artist who introduced
Monet to painting, he
became a friend and
supporter. Well before
Monet and Renoir, he was
recording the holiday
activities of bourgeois
visitors to the newly
popular resorts along the
Normandy coast.

23
MONDAY

24
TUESDAY

25
WEDNESDAY

26
THURSDAY

27
FRIDAY

28
SATURDAY

29
SUNDAY

30

MONDAY

1

TUESDAY

2

WEDNESDAY

3

THURSDAY

4

FRIDAY   Independence Day

5

SATURDAY

6

SUNDAY

JUNE

s m t w t f s
1 2 3 4 5 6 7
8 9 10 11 12 13 14
15 16 17 18 19 20 21
22 23 24 25 26 27 28
29 30

JULY

s m t w t f s
1 2 3 4 5
6 7 8 9 10 11 12
13 14 15 16 17 18 19
20 21 22 23 24 25 26
27 28 29 30 31

RENOIR
The Rowers' Lunch.
About 1879–80
Oil on canvas
CHICAGO

Rendered with irregular
dabs and strokes of paint
which replace consistent
outlining, *The Rowers'
Lunch* (at the Restaurant
Fournaise in Chatou) is the
epitome of Renoir's
Impressionist style. It
includes portraits of Aline
Charigot, Renoir's frequent
model and later his wife,
and his fellow painter and
patron Gustave Caillebotte.

JULY

s	m	t	w	t	f	s
		1	2	3	4	5
6	7	8	9	10	11	12
13	14	15	16	17	18	19
20	21	22	23	24	25	26
27	28	29	30	31		

DEGAS
*Carriage at the
Races.*   About 1870–72
Oil on canvas
BOSTON

All the Impressionists
admired Japanese
woodblock prints for their
straightforward interest in
contemporary Japanese life
and for their startlingly
cropped and composed
designs. Shown at the first
Impressionist exhibition,
Carriage at the Races
depicted the Valpinçon
family thrusting out of the
picture space—a most
Japanese device.

7
MONDAY

8
TUESDAY

9
WEDNESDAY

10
THURSDAY

11
FRIDAY

12
SATURDAY

13
SUNDAY

14
MONDAY

15
TUESDAY

16
WEDNESDAY

17
THURSDAY

18
FRIDAY

19
SATURDAY

20
SUNDAY

JULY

s	m	t	w	t	f	s
		1	2	3	4	5
6	7	8	9	10	11	12
13	14	15	16	17	18	19
20	21	22	23	24	25	26
27	28	29	30	31		

RENOIR
The Seine River at Chatou. About 1879
Oil on canvas
BOSTON

Although landscape painting formed the heart of Impressionism, Renoir was a reluctant landscapist, usually preferring figure subjects. Bright summer light flickering off swaying grasses, shimmering leaves, and rippling water, however, challenged him to create one of his most beautiful paintings from the meadows along the Seine outside Chatou.

JULY

s	m	t	w	t	f	s
		1	2	3	4	5
6	7	8	9	10	11	12
13	14	15	16	17	18	19
20	21	22	23	24	25	26
27	28	29	30	31		

RENOIR
The Grand Canal, Venice.
1881
Oil on canvas
BOSTON

The canals and unique
architecture of Venice have
guaranteed the city an
enduring popularity
among painters. For the
Impressionists, the bright
southern sun made the city
irresistible, and during an
1881 visit, Renoir made
nearly a dozen paintings of
popular motifs.

21
MONDAY

22
TUESDAY

23
WEDNESDAY

24
THURSDAY

25
FRIDAY

26
SATURDAY

27
SUNDAY

28
MONDAY

29
TUESDAY

30
WEDNESDAY

31
THURSDAY

1
FRIDAY

2
SATURDAY

3
SUNDAY

JULY

s	m	t	w	t	f	s
		1	2	3	4	5
6	7	8	9	10	11	12
13	14	15	16	17	18	19
20	21	22	23	24	25	26
27	28	29	30	31		

AUGUST

s	m	t	w	t	f	s
					1	2
3	4	5	6	7	8	9
10	11	12	13	14	15	16
17	18	19	20	21	22	23
24	25	26	27	28	29	30
31						

MONET
Grand Canal, Venice.
1908
Oil on canvas
BOSTON

Monet never shared
Renoir's interest in the
great Renaissance painters,
and he first visited Italy
late in his life—only to
regret not having come
earlier, while he was
"still full of daring." His
interpretation of the Grand
Canal balanced shimmering
buildings against the
forceful verticals of gondola
posts.

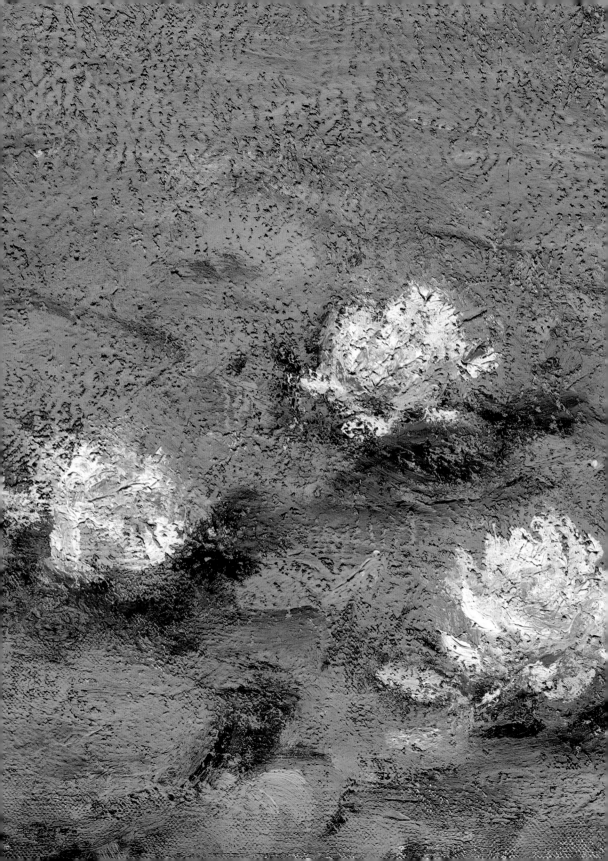

AUGUST

s	m	t	w	t	f	s
					1	2
3	4	5	6	7	8	9
10	11	12	13	14	15	16
17	18	19	20	21	22	23
24	25	26	27	28	29	30
31						

MONET
Waterlilies I.   1905
Oil on canvas
BOSTON

As Renoir frequently
turned to his family for
inspiration in his later
years, Monet turned to his
magnificent gardens in
Giverny. The ponds, with
rippling surfaces, swirling
shadows, and drifting
reflections, offered an
ever-changing, beautifully
colored world without
boundaries or spatial
constrictions.

4
MONDAY

5
TUESDAY

6
WEDNESDAY

7
THURSDAY

8
FRIDAY

9
SATURDAY

10
SUNDAY

11
MONDAY

12
TUESDAY

13
WEDNESDAY

14
THURSDAY

15
FRIDAY

16
SATURDAY

17
SUNDAY

AUGUST

s	m	t	w	t	f	s
					1	2
3	4	5	6	7	8	9
10	11	12	13	14	15	16
17	18	19	20	21	22	23
24	25	26	27	28	29	30
31						

RENOIR
Study for The Bather.
About 1884–85
Black, red, and white
chalks over graphite
CHICAGO

This almost life-size work,
executed in colored chalks,
is a preliminary study for
Renoir's great *Bathers*
of 1887, now in the
Philadelphia Museum.
It is evidence of the degree
of care with which Renoir
prepared his major
paintings in the late 1880s,
eschewing Impressionist
spontaneity for careful
drawing.

AUGUST

s m t w t f s
            1 2
3 4 5 6 7 8 9
10 11 12 13 14 15 16
17 18 19 20 21 22 23
24 25 26 27 28 29 30
31

RENOIR
*Studies of Nudes, the
Artist's Children, and His
Wife.*   About 1888
Oil on canvas
CHICAGO

Renoir often filled a single
canvas with many
unrelated sketches as an
exercise for hand and eye.
The styles on this single
canvas, for instance, range
from the exquisite
rendering of the baby in the
bonnet, which resembles a
delicate drawing, to the
powerful and sleek nudes,
which repeat in miniature
Renoir's *Bather* oil
paintings.

18
MONDAY

19
TUESDAY

20
WEDNESDAY

21
THURSDAY

22
FRIDAY

23
SATURDAY

24
SUNDAY

25
MONDAY

26
TUESDAY

27
WEDNESDAY

28
THURSDAY

29
FRIDAY

30
SATURDAY

31
SUNDAY

AUGUST

s	m	t	w	t	f	s
					1	2
3	4	5	6	7	8	9
10	11	12	13	14	15	16
17	18	19	20	21	22	23
24	25	26	27	28	29	30
31						

RENOIR
Children on the Seashore at Guernsey.   About 1883
Oil on canvas
BOSTON

The Normandy Coast and the Channel Islands, such as Guernsey, enjoyed great popularity among holiday-goers in the late nineteenth century. Several of Renoir's friends and patrons spent summer months at the seashore and often included him in their parties, which he recorded with evident pleasure.

SEPTEMBER

s	m	t	w	t	f	s
	1	2	3	4	5	6
7	8	9	10	11	12	13
14	15	16	17	18	19	20
21	22	23	24	25	26	27
28	29	30				

RENOIR
*Children on the Seashore at
Guernsey.*   About 1883
Oil on canvas
BOSTON

Bathers splashing amid the
rocky cliffs of Guernsey
form the backdrop for a
casually posed portrait of
four children. Renoir's visit
to Guernsey in September
of 1883 produced a number
of landscape sketches which
he adapted for larger,
finished paintings after his
return to Paris.

Labor Day

1
MONDAY

2
TUESDAY

3
WEDNESDAY

4
THURSDAY

5
FRIDAY

6
SATURDAY

7
SUNDAY

8
MONDAY

9
TUESDAY

10
WEDNESDAY

11
THURSDAY

12
FRIDAY

13
SATURDAY

14
SUNDAY

SEPTEMBER

s	m	t	w	t	f	s
		1	2	3	4	5	6
7	8	9	10	11	12	13
14	15	16	17	18	19	20
21	22	23	24	25	26	27
28	29	30				

RENOIR
Girls Picking Flowers in a Meadow. About 1890
Oil on canvas
BOSTON

In many of Renoir's paintings of young girls colorfully dressed and contentedly absorbed in simple entertainments, the landscape became little more than a delicately colored backdrop. Impressionist fidelity to nature was subordinated to Renoir's interest in the human figure.

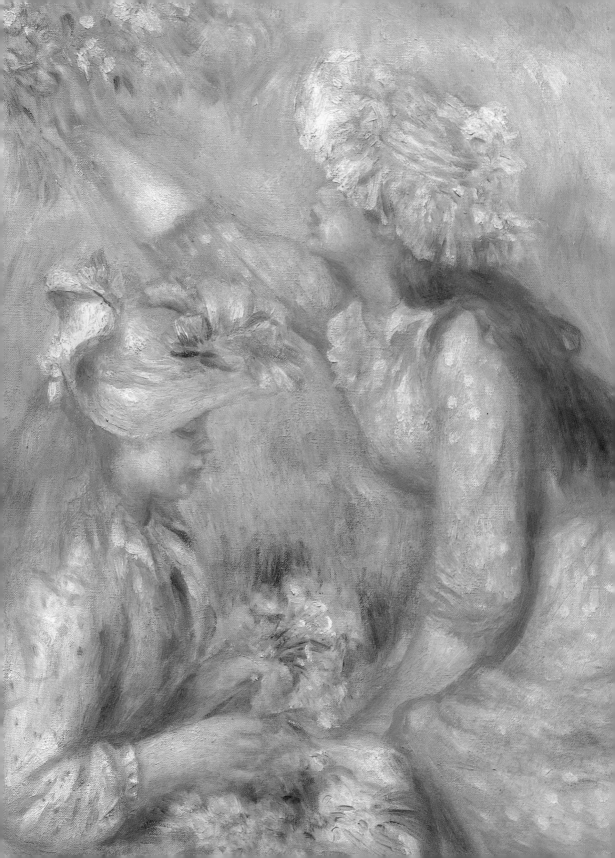

SEPTEMBER

s	m	t	w	t	f	s
		1	2	3	4	5	6
7	8	9	10	11	12	13
14	15	16	17	18	19	20
21	22	23	24	25	26	27
28	29	30				

MORISOT
White Flowers in a Bowl.
1885
Oil on canvas
BOSTON

Berthe Morisot, one of two
women associated with the
Impressionist group and a
consistent participant in the
Impressionist exhibitions,
became a particularly close
friend of Renoir. They
frequently shared models,
and her daughter, Julie
Manet, who posed for
Renoir, wrote a diary with
important reminiscences of
Renoir and his work.

15
MONDAY

16
TUESDAY

17
WEDNESDAY

18
THURSDAY

19
FRIDAY

20
SATURDAY

21
SUNDAY

22
MONDAY

23
TUESDAY

24
WEDNESDAY

25
THURSDAY

26
FRIDAY

27
SATURDAY

28
SUNDAY

SEPTEMBER
s m t w t f s
      1 2 3 4 5 6
7 8 9 10 11 12 13
14 15 16 17 18 19 20
21 22 23 24 25 26 27
28 29 30

CAILLEBOTTE
Fruit Displayed on a Stand.
About 1881–82
Oil on canvas
BOSTON

Less well known than the
other Impressionists,
Caillebotte is usually
remembered for his large
bequest of Impressionist
paintings, which forms the
core of the Louvre's
Impressionist collection.
But his own best pictures
are among the most original
by any Impressionist.
Fruit, piled high on the
vendor's stand, brilliantly
updates still-life painting
design.

SEPTEMBER

s m t w t f s
      1 2 3 4 5 6
 7 8 9 10 11 12 13
14 15 16 17 18 19 20
21 22 23 24 25 26 27
28 29 30

OCTOBER

s m t w t f s
          1 2 3 4
 5 6 7 8 9 10 11
12 13 14 15 16 17 18
19 20 21 22 23 24 25
26 27 28 29 30 31

RENOIR
*Mixed Flowers in an
Earthenware Pot.* 1869
Oil on canvas
BOSTON

During the summer of
1869, Renoir lived with his
parents in Louveciennes, a
few miles from Monet's
summer home in Bougival.
Just as the two artists often
painted landscapes side by
side, so they both tackled
the same pot of flowers and
fruits. In *Mixed Flowers*,
Renoir began to abandon
his earlier delicate, precise
brushwork for a more
boldly realized technique.

29
MONDAY

30
TUESDAY

1
WEDNESDAY

2
THURSDAY

3
FRIDAY

Rosh Hashanah Begins (Sundown)

4
SATURDAY

5
SUNDAY

6
MONDAY

7
TUESDAY

8
WEDNESDAY

9
THURSDAY

10
FRIDAY

11
SATURDAY

12
SUNDAY

Columbus Day
Yom Kippur (Sundown)

OCTOBER
s m t w t f s
1 2 3 4
5 6 7 8 9 10 11
12 13 14 15 16 17 18
19 20 21 22 23 24 25
26 27 28 29 30 31

RAFFAELLI
Garlic Seller.   About 1880
Oil on paper mounted and
extended on canvas
BOSTON

Raffaelli exhibited in two
Impressionist group shows,
under the aegis of Degas,
although Monet and Renoir
were skeptical that he was
really an Impressionist.
While Raffaelli's anecdotal
subject matter was old-
fashioned by the 1880s,
he did share the
Impressionists' interest in
recording the real Paris,
with its smokestacks and its
no-man's-land of
developing industry.

OCTOBER

s	m	t	w	t	f	s
			1	2	3	4
5	6	7	8	9	10	11
12	13	14	15	16	17	18
19	20	21	22	23	24	25
26	27	28	29	30	31	

13
MONDAY

Columbus Day Observed

14
TUESDAY

15
WEDNESDAY

RENOIR
Fruits from the Midi.   1881
Oil on canvas
CHICAGO

Renoir once remarked that
he tried to paint human
beings just as he would
beautiful fruit; and he
could just as readily imbue
his still lifes with the same
sense of abundant luxury
found in his paintings of
voluptuous nudes. This
glowing canvas is a lush
reminder of the harvests of
the sun-drenched south of
France.

16
THURSDAY

17
FRIDAY

18
SATURDAY

19
SUNDAY

20
MONDAY

21
TUESDAY

22
WEDNESDAY

23
THURSDAY

24
FRIDAY

25
SATURDAY

26
SUNDAY   Daylight Saving Ends

OCTOBER

s	m	t	w	t	f	s
			1	2	3	4
5	6	7	8	9	10	11
12	13	14	15	16	17	18
19	20	21	22	23	24	25
26	27	28	29	30	31	

DIAZ DE LA PEÑA
Flowers.   About 1860
Oil on canvas
BOSTON

Diaz, one of the generation
of artists before the
Impressionists, became a
supportive friend to Renoir
in his early career. He too
had started as a porcelain
painter, and he favored
similar subjects: flowers,
costume pictures, charming
scenes of flirtation. Most
important for Renoir was
Diaz's use of bright color
and distinctive, heavily
impastoed brushwork.

OCTOBER

s	m	t	w	t	f	s
			1	2	3	4
5	6	7	8	9	10	11
12	13	14	15	16	17	18
19	20	21	22	23	24	25
26	27	28	29	30	31	

NOVEMBER

s	m	t	w	t	f	s
						1
2	3	4	5	6	7	8
9	10	11	12	13	14	15
16	17	18	19	20	21	22
23	24	25	26	27	28	29
30						

MONET
Haystack at Sunset near Giverny. 1891
Oil on canvas
BOSTON

In the *Haystack* series, Monet confronted the same concern that had driven Renoir back to figure-centered paintings, and to nudes in particular: the difficulty of creating convincing, three-dimensional reality without sacrificing the brilliant colors and flickering paint touches of Impressionism.

27
MONDAY

28
TUESDAY

29
WEDNESDAY

30
THURSDAY

31
FRIDAY

Hallowe'en

1
SATURDAY

2
SUNDAY

3
MONDAY

4
TUESDAY   Election Day

5
WEDNESDAY

6
THURSDAY

7
FRIDAY

8
SATURDAY

9
SUNDAY

NOVEMBER

s	m	t	w	t	f	s
						1
2	3	4	5	6	7	8
9	10	11	12	13	14	15
16	17	18	19	20	21	22
23	24	25	26	27	28	29
30						

TOULOUSE-LAUTREC
At the Café La Mie.   1891
Watercolor and gouache
on paper mounted on
millboard mounted on
panel
BOSTON

Toulouse-Lautrec was more
than twenty years younger
than Renoir and his
Impressionist
contemporaries, but
Lautrec greatly admired
the older artists' work.
However, while he
continued their interest in
strong color and distinctive,
assertive brushwork, he
saw the social interactions
of modern society with a
more jaundiced eye.

NOVEMBER

s	m	t	w	t	f	s
						1
2	3	4	5	6	7	8
9	10	11	12	13	14	15
16	17	18	19	20	21	22
23	24	25	26	27	28	29
30						

RENOIR
Lucie Bérard: Child in White. 1883
Oil on canvas
CHICAGO

Paul Bérard, a good friend of Renoir's, commissioned from him several portraits of his children. Here Renoir has captured the charm and vulnerability of Lucie Bérard behind the formality of her pose and her expensive white coat.

10
MONDAY

11
TUESDAY

Veterans' Day

12
WEDNESDAY

13
THURSDAY

14
FRIDAY

15
SATURDAY

16
SUNDAY

17
MONDAY

18
TUESDAY

19
WEDNESDAY

20
THURSDAY

21
FRIDAY

22
SATURDAY

23
SUNDAY

NOVEMBER

s	m	t	w	t	f	s
						1
2	3	4	5	6	7	8
9	10	11	12	13	14	15
16	17	18	19	20	21	22
23	24	25	26	27	28	29
30						

DEGAS
Edmondo and Thérèse Morbili.   About 1867
Oil on canvas
BOSTON

Unlike Renoir, Degas did not have to seek portrait commissions outside his own family and social circle. Choosing his own subjects allowed him greater freedom to explore psychological nuances and contrasts between individuals. His subdued palette, often balanced in the 1860s, as was Manet's, around a range of blacks and grays, adds to the somber intensity of his portrait of his sister and brother-in-law.

NOVEMBER

s	m	t	w	t	f	s
						1
2	3	4	5	6	7	8
9	10	11	12	13	14	15
16	17	18	19	20	21	22
23	24	25	26	27	28	29
30						

PISSARRO
The Turkey Girl.   1884
Gouache on composition
board
BOSTON

By 1884, Pissarro shared
Renoir's concern that the
Impressionist technique
was producing confusing
landscapes that lacked real
volume. By introducing
larger figures in his work,
he hoped to add greater
three-dimensionality to
contrast with the simple
spaces.

24
MONDAY

25
TUESDAY

26
WEDNESDAY

27
THURSDAY

Thanksgiving Day

28
FRIDAY

29
SATURDAY

30
SUNDAY

1

MONDAY

2

TUESDAY

3

WEDNESDAY

4

THURSDAY

5

FRIDAY

6

SATURDAY

7

SUNDAY

DECEMBER

s	m	t	w	t	f	s
		1	2	3	4	5	6
7	8	9	10	11	12	13
14	15	16	17	18	19	20
21	22	23	24	25	26	27
28	29	30	31			

RENOIR
Gabrielle and Coco Playing Dominoes. About 1905
Oil on canvas
BOSTON

Coco (a nickname for Renoir's youngest son, Claude) provided subject matter for many of the scenes of family life that filled the artist's last years. Increasingly crippled by rheumatoid arthritis, Renoir was determined nonetheless to find, and give, pleasure with his painting.

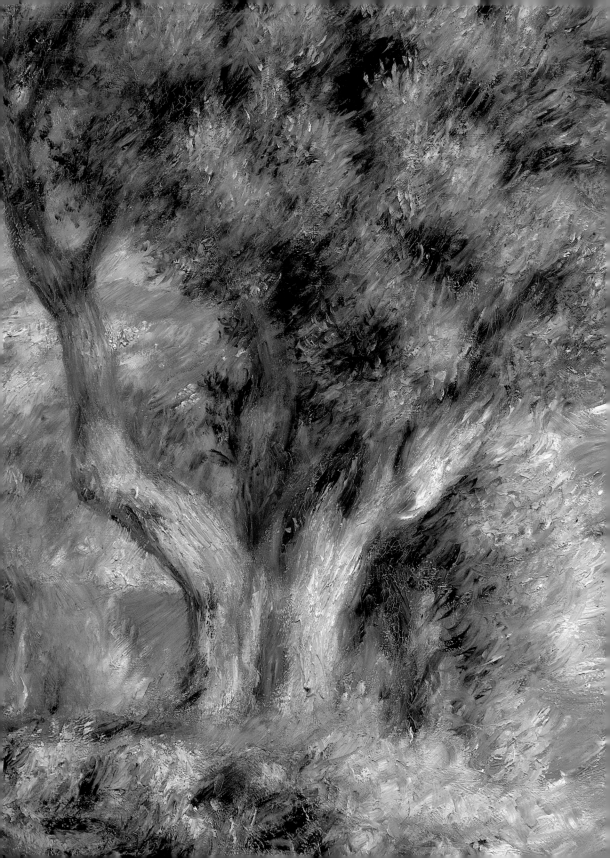

DECEMBER

s	m	t	w	t	f	s
		1	2	3	4	5	6
7	8	9	10	11	12	13
14	15	16	17	18	19	20
21	22	23	24	25	26	27
28	29	30	31			

RENOIR
*Landscape on the Coast
near Menton.* 1883
Oil on canvas
BOSTON

Monet and Renoir visited
the south of France together
in December 1883, and
many of Renoir's great
landscapes date from this
trip. Although Monet now
found it difficult to paint in
Renoir's presence, Renoir
began several pictures,
exploring the variety of
hues that distinguished the
Mediterranean landscape
from areas more familiar
to him.

8
MONDAY

9
TUESDAY

10
WEDNESDAY

11
THURSDAY

12
FRIDAY

13
SATURDAY

14
SUNDAY

15

MONDAY

16

TUESDAY

17

WEDNESDAY

18

THURSDAY

19

FRIDAY

20

SATURDAY

21

SUNDAY

DECEMBER

s m t w t f s
          1 2 3 4 5 6
 7 8 9 10 11 12 13
14 15 16 17 18 19 20
21 22 23 24 25 26 27
28 29 30 31

MONET
Cap Martin, near Menton.
1884
Oil on canvas
BOSTON

Although Monet was enamored of the landscape and bright sunlight when he visited the Riviera with Renoir in 1883, he felt too constrained by Renoir's presence to paint. Instead, he returned alone, later, to paint landscapes with powerful contrasts of color and texture, where Renoir had found harmonies and a more unified landscape (see preceding week).

Claude Monet 8.

DECEMBER

s	m	t	w	t	f	s
	1	2	3	4	5	6
7	8	9	10	11	12	13
14	15	16	17	18	19	20
21	22	23	24	25	26	27
28	29	30	31			

RENOIR
Lady at the Piano. 1875
Oil on canvas
CHICAGO

Renoir often painted genre scenes of contemporary bourgeois life, usually preferring women or girls in intimate, domestic settings. Here, the piano and the opulence of the young woman's blue-white dress and the furnishings around her suggest a well-to-do household. The unusual perspective, with the viewer slightly above the figure, and the diffused candlelight over the forms, bring a traditional theme into the realm of Impressionism.

22
MONDAY

23
TUESDAY

24
WEDNESDAY

Christmas Day

25
THURSDAY

Chanukkah Begins (Sundown)

26
FRIDAY

27
SATURDAY

28
SUNDAY

29
MONDAY

30
TUESDAY

31
WEDNESDAY   New Year's Eve

1
THURSDAY   New Year's Day

2
FRIDAY

3
SATURDAY

4
SUNDAY

DECEMBER

s m t w t f s
1 2 3 4 5 6
7 8 9 10 11 12 13
14 15 16 17 18 19 20
21 22 23 24 25 26 27
28 29 30 31

JANUARY

s m t w t f s
1 2 3
4 5 6 7 8 9 10
11 12 13 14 15 16 17
18 19 20 21 22 23 24
25 26 27 28 29 30 31

RENOIR
The Artist's Son Jean.
1900
Oil on canvas
CHICAGO

This portrait of Renoir's second son, Jean (later a famous French film director), playing with an embroidered handkerchief emphasizes his red-blond hair, high coloring, and rounded physique in an echo of such Renaissance and Baroque masters as Titian and Rubens, both of whom strongly influenced Renoir.

Index

RENOIR
Near the Lake.
About 1880
Oil on canvas
CHICAGO

Two figures relax in the
shade of a bower, lost in,
but not obscured by, the
lavish foliage. This delicate
balance between figure and
landscape, characteristic of
other paintings from this
period, represents Renoir's
last Impressionist series
before he turned his
attention almost completely
to the solidity of the human
figure.

BOUDIN, EUGÈNE-LOUIS (1824–98)

*Beach Scene with Fashionably Dressed
Figures.* 1865
Oil on panel, 14 × 22⅝ in.
Gift of Mr. and Mrs. John J. Wilson.
Museum of Fine Arts, Boston

CAILLEBOTTE, GUSTAVE (1848–94)

Fruit Displayed on a Stand. About
1881–82
Oil on canvas, 30⅛ × 39⅝ in.
Purchase, Fannie P. Mason Fund.
Museum of Fine Arts, Boston

*Paris, A Rainy Day (Intersection of the
Rue de Turin and Rue de Moscou).*
1877
Oil on canvas, 83½ × 108¾ in.
Charles H. and Mary F.S. Worcester
Fund. © The Art Institute of
Chicago. All Rights Reserved

DEGAS, EDGAR (1834–1917)

Carriage at the Races. About 1870–72
Oil on canvas, 14⅜ × 22 in.
Purchase, 1931 Purchase Fund.
Museum of Fine Arts, Boston

Dancer. About 1878
Pastel on paper, 30¼ × 17¾ in.
Purchase, 1931 Purchase Fund.
Museum of Fine Arts, Boston

Edmondo and Thérèse Morbili.
About 1867
    Oil on canvas, 45⅞ × 34¾ in.
    Gift of Robert Treat Paine II.
    Museum of Fine Arts, Boston

Race Horses at Longchamp.
About 1873–75
    Oil on canvas, 13⅜ × 16½ in.
    S.A. Denio Collection (Purchase,
    Sylvanus Adams Denio Fund) 1903.
    Museum of Fine Arts, Boston

DIAZ DE LA PEÑA, NARCISSE-VIRGILE
(1808–76)

Flowers. About 1860
    Oil on canvas, 15¾ × 9⅞ in.
    Bequest of Alan F. Mosley through
    Margaret LeMoyne Wentworth and
    Helen Freeman Hull. Museum of
    Fine Arts, Boston

FANTIN-LATOUR, HENRI (1836–1904)

Flowers and Fruit on a Table.
1865
    Oil on canvas, 23⅝ × 28⅞ in.
    Bequest of John T. Spaulding.
    Museum of Fine Arts, Boston

MANET, EDOUARD (1832–83)

The Street Singer. 1862
    Oil on canvas, 68⅝ × 42½ in.
    Bequest of Sarah Choate Sears in
    memory of her husband, Joshua
    Montgomery Sears. Museum of Fine
    Arts, Boston

MONET, CLAUDE (1840–1926)

*Boulevard St.-Denis, Argenteuil, in
Winter.* 1875
    Oil on canvas, 24 × 32⅛ in.
    Gift of Richard Saltonstall. Museum
    of Fine Arts, Boston

*Camille Monet and a Child in the
Artist's Garden in Argenteuil.* 1875
    Oil on canvas, 21¾ × 25½ in.
    Anonymous gift in memory of Mr.
    and Mrs. Edwin S. Webster.
    Museum of Fine Arts, Boston

Cap Martin, near Menton. 1884
    Oil on canvas, 25¾ × 31⅞ in.
    Juliana Cheney Edwards Collection.
    Bequest of Robert J. Edwards, and
    gift of Hannah Marcy Edwards and
    Grace M. Edwards in memory of
    their mother. Museum of Fine Arts,
    Boston

Grand Canal, Venice. 1908
    Oil on canvas, 29 × 36⅜ in.
    Bequest of Alexander Cochrane.
    Museum of Fine Arts, Boston

Haystack at Sunset near Giverny. 1891
    Oil on canvas, 28⅞ × 36½ in.
    Juliana Cheney Edwards Collection.
    Bequest of Robert J. Edwards in
    memory of his mother. Museum of
    Fine Arts, Boston

Monet's House at Argenteuil. 1873
    Oil on canvas, 23¹¹⁄₁₆ × 28⅞ in.
    Mr. and Mrs. Martin A. Ryerson
    Collection. © The Art Institute of
    Chicago. All Rights Reserved

Rouen Cathedral at Dawn. 1894
    Oil on canvas, 41¾ × 29⅛ in.
    Tompkins Collection. Purchase,
    Arthur Gordon Tompkins Residuary
    Fund. Museum of Fine Arts, Boston

Snow at Argenteuil. About 1874
    Oil on canvas, 21½ × 29 in.
    Bequest of Anna Perkins Rogers.
    Museum of Fine Arts, Boston

Waterlilies I. 1905
    Oil on canvas, 35¼ × 39½ in.
    Gift of Edward Jackson Holmes.
    Museum of Fine Arts, Boston

MORISOT, BERTHE (1841–95)

White Flowers in a Bowl. 1885
    Oil on canvas, 18⅛ × 21⅝ in.
    Bequest of John T. Spaulding.
    Museum of Fine Arts, Boston

PISSARRO, CAMILLE (1830–1903)

Poultry Market at Gisors. 1885
    Gouache and black chalk on paper

mounted on canvas, 32⅜ × 32⅜ in. Bequest of John T. Spaulding. Museum of Fine Arts, Boston

The Turkey Girl. 1884
Gouache on composition board, 31⅞ × 24¾ in. Juliana Cheney Edwards Collection. Bequest of Hannah Marcy Edwards in memory of her mother. Museum of Fine Arts, Boston

Woman and Child at the Well. 1882
Oil on canvas, 32⅛ × 26⅛ in. Potter Palmer Collection. © The Art Institute of Chicago. All Rights Reserved

RAFFAELLI, JEAN-FRANÇOIS (1850–1924)

Garlic Seller. About 1880
Oil on paper mounted and extended on canvas, 28¼ × 19¼ in. Henry C. and Martha B. Angell Collection (Gift of Martha B. Angell). Museum of Fine Arts, Boston

RENOIR, PIERRE-AUGUSTE (1841–1919)

Alfred Sisley. About 1875–76
Oil on canvas, 26⅛ × 21⁹/₁₆ in. Mr. and Mrs. Lewis Larned Coburn Memorial Collection. © The Art Institute of Chicago. All Rights Reserved

Algerian Girl. 1881
Oil on canvas, 20 × 16 in. Juliana Cheney Edwards Collection. Bequest of Hannah Marcy Edwards in memory of her mother. Museum of Fine Arts, Boston

The Artist's Son Jean. 1900.
Oil on canvas, 22 × 18¼ in. Mr. and Mrs. Martin A. Ryerson Collection. © The Art Institute of Chicago. All Rights Reserved

The Boating Couple. About 1881
Pastel on paper, 17¾ × 23 in. Given in memory of Governor Alvan

T. Fuller by the Fuller Foundation. Museum of Fine Arts, Boston

Children on the Seashore at Guernsey. About 1883
Oil on canvas, 36 × 26¼ in. Bequest of John T. Spaulding. Museum of Fine Arts, Boston

Dance at Bougival. 1883
Oil on canvas, 70 × 37¾ in. Purchase, Anna Mitchell Richards Fund and Contributions. Museum of Fine Arts, Boston

Fruits from the Midi. 1881
Oil on canvas, 19¹⁵/₁₆ × 25¹¹/₁₆ in. Mr. and Mrs. Martin A. Ryerson Collection. © The Art Institute of Chicago. All Rights Reserved

Gabrielle and Coco Playing Dominoes. About 1905
Oil on canvas, 20½ × 18⅛ in. Given in memory of Governor Alvan T. Fuller by the Fuller Foundation. Museum of Fine Arts, Boston

Girls Picking Flowers in a Meadow. About 1890
Oil on canvas, 25⅝ × 31⅞ in. Juliana Cheney Edwards Collection. Bequest of Hannah Marcy Edwards in memory of her mother. Museum of Fine Arts, Boston

The Grand Canal, Venice. 1881
Oil on canvas, 21¼ × 25½ in. Bequest of Alexander Cochrane. Museum of Fine Arts, Boston

Lady at the Piano. 1875
Oil on canvas, 36⅝ × 29½ in. Mr. and Mrs. Martin A. Ryerson Collection. © The Art Institute of Chicago. All Rights Reserved

Lady Sewing. 1879
Oil on canvas, 24³/₁₆ × 19¹³/₁₆ in. Mr. and Mrs. Lewis Larned Coburn Memorial Collection. © The Art Institute of Chicago. All Rights Reserved

Landscape on the Coast near Menton.
1883
    Oil on canvas, 26 × 32⅛ in.
    Bequest of John T. Spaulding.
    Museum of Fine Arts, Boston

Lucie Bérard: Child in White. 1883
    Oil on canvas, 24¼ × 19¾ in.
    Mr. and Mrs. Martin A. Ryerson
    Collection. © The Art Institute of
    Chicago. All Rights Reserved

Madame Clapisson (Lady with a Fan).
1883
    Oil on canvas, 32⅝ × 25⅝ in.
    Mr. and Mrs. Martin A. Ryerson
    Collection. © The Art Institute of
    Chicago. All Rights Reserved

Mixed Flowers in an Earthenware Pot.
1869
    Oil on canvas, 25½ × 21⅜ in.
    Bequest of John T. Spaulding.
    Museum of Fine Arts, Boston

Near the Lake. About 1880
    Oil on canvas, 18¹¹/₁₆ × 22⅜ in.
    Potter Palmer Collection. © The
    Art Institute of Chicago. All Rights
    Reserved

On the Terrace. 1881
    Oil on canvas, 39⁹/₁₆ × 31⅞ in.
    Mr. and Mrs. Lewis Larned Coburn
    Memorial Collection. © The Art
    Institute of Chicago. All Rights
    Reserved

Rocky Crags at L'Estaque. 1882
    Oil on canvas, 26⅛ × 31⅞ in.
    Juliana Cheney Edwards Collection.
    Bequest of Hannah Marcy Edwards
    in memory of her mother. Museum
    of Fine Arts, Boston

The Rowers' Lunch. About 1879–80
    Oil on canvas, 21¹¹/₁₆ × 25¹⁵/₁₆ in.
    Potter Palmer Collection. © The
    Art Institute of Chicago. All Rights
    Reserved

The Seine River at Chatou. About 1879
    Oil on canvas, 28⅞ × 36⅜ in.

Gift of Arthur B. Emmons. Museum
of Fine Arts, Boston

*Studies of Nudes, the Artist's
Children, and His Wife.* About 1888
    Oil on canvas, 18⅛ × 15⁷/₁₆ in.
    Phillips Family Collection restricted
    gift. © The Art Institute of
    Chicago. All Rights Reserved

Study for The Bather. About 1884–85
    Black, red, and white chalks over
    graphite, 38⅝ × 25³/₁₆ in.
    Bequest of Kate L. Brewster. © The
    Art Institute of Chicago. All Rights
    Reserved

Two Little Circus Girls. 1879
    Oil on canvas, 51¾ × 39⅛ in.
    Potter Palmer Collection. © The
    Art Institute of Chicago. All Rights
    Reserved

*Woman with a Parasol and a Small
Child on a Sunlit Hillside.* About 1874
    Oil on canvas, 18½ × 22⅛ in.
    Bequest of John T. Spaulding.
    Museum of Fine Arts, Boston

SEURAT, GEORGES (1859–91)

*Sunday Afternoon on the Island of La
Grande-Jatte.* 1884–86
    Oil on canvas, 81¾ × 21¼ in.
    Helen Birch Bartlett Memorial
    Collection. © The Art Institute of
    Chicago. All Rights Reserved

TOULOUSE-LAUTREC, HENRI DE (1864–1901)

At the Café La Mie. 1891
    Watercolor and gouache on paper
    mounted on millboard mounted on
    panel, 20⅞ × 26¾ in.
    S.A. Denio Collection (Purchase,
    Sylvanus Adams Denio Fund and
    General Income) 1940. Museum of
    Fine Arts, Boston

At the Moulin Rouge. 1892
    Oil on canvas, 48⁷/₁₆ × 55½ in.
    Helen Birch Bartlett Memorial
    Collection. © The Art Institute of
    Chicago. All Rights Reserved

JANUARY	FEBRUARY	MARCH
1	1	1
2	2	2
3	3	3
4	4	4
5	5	5
6	6	6
7	7	7
8	8	8
9	9	9
10	10	10
11	11	11
12	12	12
13	13	13
14	14	14
15	15	15
16	16	16
17	17	17
18	18	18
19	19	19
20	20	20
21	21	21
22	22	22
23	23	23
24	24	24
25	25	25
26	26	26
27	27	27
28	28	28
29		29
30		30
31		31

APRIL	MAY	JUNE
1	1	1
2	2	2
3	3	3
4	4	4
5	5	5
6	6	6
7	7	7
8	8	8
9	9	9
10	10	10
11	11	11
12	12	12
13	13	13
14	14	14
15	15	15
16	16	16
17	17	17
18	18	18
19	19	19
20	20	20
21	21	21
22	22	22
23	23	23
24	24	24
25	25	25
26	26	26
27	27	27
28	28	28
29	29	29
30	30	30
	31	

JULY	AUGUST	SEPTEMBER
1	1	1
2	2	2
3	3	3
4	4	4
5	5	5
6	6	6
7	7	7
8	8	8
9	9	9
10	10	10
11	11	11
12	12	12
13	13	13
14	14	14
15	15	15
16	16	16
17	17	17
18	18	18
19	19	19
20	20	20
21	21	21
22	22	22
23	23	23
24	24	24
25	25	25
26	26	26
27	27	27
28	28	28
29	29	29
30	30	30
31	31	

OCTOBER	NOVEMBER	DECEMBER
1	1	1
2	2	2
3	3	3
4	4	4
5	5	5
6	6	6
7	7	7
8	8	8
9	9	9
10	10	10
11	11	11
12	12	12
13	13	13
14	14	14
15	15	15
16	16	16
17	17	17
18	18	18
19	19	19
20	20	20
21	21	21
22	22	22
23	23	23
24	24	24
25	25	25
26	26	26
27	27	27
28	28	28
29	29	29
30	30	30
31		31

BIRTHDAYS

ANNIVERSARIES

SPECIAL DATES

FREQUENTLY CALLED PHONE NUMBERS

YUET CHAN   176-18 90TH AVE. JAMAICA, NY 11432

IMPORTANT PHONE NUMBERS

POLICE

DOCTOR

DENTIST

FIRE DEPT.

AMBULANCE

HOSPITAL

NOTES

NOTES

NOTES

NOTES

NOTES

1985

JANUARY	FEBRUARY	MARCH	APRIL	MAY	JUNE
s m t w t f s	s m t w t f s	s m t w t f s	s m t w t f s	s m t w t f s	s m t w t f s
1 2 3 4 5	1 2	1 2	1 2 3 4 5 6	1 2 3 4	1
6 7 8 9 10 11 12	3 4 5 6 7 8 9	3 4 5 6 7 8 9	7 8 9 10 11 12 13	5 6 7 8 9 10 11	2 3 4 5 6 7 8
13 14 15 16 17 18 19	10 11 12 13 14 15 16	10 11 12 13 14 15 16	14 15 16 17 18 19 20	12 13 14 15 16 17 18	9 10 11 12 13 14 15
20 21 22 23 24 25 26	17 18 19 20 21 22 23	17 18 19 20 21 22 23	21 22 23 24 25 26 27	19 20 21 22 23 24 25	16 17 18 19 20 21 22
27 28 29 30 31	24 25 26 27 28	24 25 26 27 28 29 30	28 29 30	26 27 28 29 30 31	23 24 25 26 27 28 29
		31			30

JULY	AUGUST	SEPTEMBER	OCTOBER	NOVEMBER	DECEMBER
s m t w t f s	s m t w t f s	s m t w t f s	s m t w t f s	s m t w t f s	s m t w t f s
1 2 3 4 5 6	1 2 3	1 2 3 4 5 6 7	1 2 3 4 5	1 2	1 2 3 4 5 6 7
7 8 9 10 11 12 13	4 5 6 7 8 9 10	8 9 10 11 12 13 14	6 7 8 9 10 11 12	3 4 5 6 7 8 9	8 9 10 11 12 13 14
14 15 16 17 18 19 20	11 12 13 14 15 16 17	15 16 17 18 19 20 21	13 14 15 16 17 18 19	10 11 12 13 14 15 16	15 16 17 18 19 20 21
21 22 23 24 25 26 27	18 19 20 21 22 23 24	22 23 24 25 26 27 28	20 21 22 23 24 25 26	17 18 19 20 21 22 23	22 23 24 25 26 27 28
28 29 30 31	25 26 27 28 29 30 31	29 30	27 28 29 30 31	24 25 26 27 28 29 30	29 30 31

1986

JANUARY	FEBRUARY	MARCH	APRIL	MAY	JUNE
s m t w t f s	s m t w t f s	s m t w t f s	s m t w t f s	s m t w t f s	s m t w t f s
1 2 3 4	1	1	1 2 3 4 5	1 2 3	1 2 3 4 5 6 7
5 6 7 8 9 10 11	2 3 4 5 6 7 8	2 3 4 5 6 7 8	6 7 8 9 10 11 12	4 5 6 7 8 9 10	8 9 10 11 12 13 14
12 13 14 15 16 17 18	9 10 11 12 13 14 15	9 10 11 12 13 14 15	13 14 15 16 17 18 19	11 12 13 14 15 16 17	15 16 17 18 19 20 21
19 20 21 22 23 24 25	16 17 18 19 20 21 22	16 17 18 19 20 21 22	20 21 22 23 24 25 26	18 19 20 21 22 23 24	22 23 24 25 26 27 28
26 27 28 29 30 31	23 24 25 26 27 28	23 24 25 26 27 28 29	27 28 29 30	25 26 27 28 29 30 31	29 30
		30 31			

JULY	AUGUST	SEPTEMBER	OCTOBER	NOVEMBER	DECEMBER
s m t w t f s	s m t w t f s	s m t w t f s	s m t w t f s	s m t w t f s	s m t w t f s
1 2 3 4 5	1 2	1 2 3 4 5 6	1 2 3 4	1	1 2 3 4 5 6
6 7 8 9 10 11 12	3 4 5 6 7 8 9	7 8 9 10 11 12 13	5 6 7 8 9 10 11	2 3 4 5 6 7 8	7 8 9 10 11 12 13
13 14 15 16 17 18 19	10 11 12 13 14 15 16	14 15 16 17 18 19 20	12 13 14 15 16 17 18	9 10 11 12 13 14 15	14 15 16 17 18 19 20
20 21 22 23 24 25 26	17 18 19 20 21 22 23	21 22 23 24 25 26 27	19 20 21 22 23 24 25	16 17 18 19 20 21 22	21 22 23 24 25 26 27
27 28 29 30 31	24 25 26 27 28 29 30	28 29 30	26 27 28 29 30 31	23 24 25 26 27 28 29	28 29 30 31
	31			30	

1987

JANUARY	FEBRUARY	MARCH	APRIL	MAY	JUNE
s m t w t f s	s m t w t f s	s m t w t f s	s m t w t f s	s m t w t f s	s m t w t f s
1 2 3	1 2 3 4 5 6 7	1 2 3 4 5 6 7	1 2 3 4	1 2	1 2 3 4 5 6
4 5 6 7 8 9 10	8 9 10 11 12 13 14	8 9 10 11 12 13 14	5 6 7 8 9 10 11	3 4 5 6 7 8 9	7 8 9 10 11 12 13
11 12 13 14 15 16 17	15 16 17 18 19 20 21	15 16 17 18 19 20 21	12 13 14 15 16 17 18	10 11 12 13 14 15 16	14 15 16 17 18 19 20
18 19 20 21 22 23 24	22 23 24 25 26 27 28	22 23 24 25 26 27 28	19 20 21 22 23 24 25	17 18 19 20 21 22 23	21 22 23 24 25 26 27
25 26 27 28 29 30 31		29 30 31	26 27 28 29 30	24 25 26 27 28 29 30	28 29 30
				31	

JULY	AUGUST	SEPTEMBER	OCTOBER	NOVEMBER	DECEMBER
s m t w t f s	s m t w t f s	s m t w t f s	s m t w t f s	s m t w t f s	s m t w t f s
1 2 3 4	1	1 2 3 4 5	1 2 3	1 2 3 4 5 6 7	1 2 3 4 5
5 6 7 8 9 10 11	2 3 4 5 6 7 8	6 7 8 9 10 11 12	4 5 6 7 8 9 10	8 9 10 11 12 13 14	6 7 8 9 10 11 12
12 13 14 15 16 17 18	9 10 11 12 13 14 15	13 14 15 16 17 18 19	11 12 13 14 15 16 17	15 16 17 18 19 20 21	13 14 15 16 17 18 19
19 20 21 22 23 24 25	16 17 18 19 20 21 22	20 21 22 23 24 25 26	18 19 20 21 22 23 24	22 23 24 25 26 27 28	20 21 22 23 24 25 26
26 27 28 29 30 31	23 24 25 26 27 28 29	27 28 29 30	25 26 27 28 29 30 31	29 30	27 28 29 30 31
	30 31				